EGMONT

We bring stories to life

First published in 2018 by Egmont UK Limited
The Yellow Building, 1 Nicholas Road, London W11 4AN
www.egmont.co.uk

Additional text by Helen Archer
Designed by Pritty Ramjee

ISBN 978 1 4052 9195 8
68939/001
Printed in the UK

WINNIE-THE-POOH

LITTLE SOMETHINGS
& SMACKERELS
FOR FOOD LOVERS

A.A.MILNE
with decorations by E.H.SHEPARD

EGMONT

WINNIE~THE~POOH

INTRODUCTION

'What do you like doing best in the world, Pooh?'
'Well,' said Pooh ... 'What I like best in the whole
world is Me and Piglet going to see You, and You
saying, "What about a little something?"
and Me saying, "Well, I shouldn't mind a little
something, should you, Piglet."'

When walking around the Hundred Acre Wood,
Pooh often finds himself feeling slightly peckish.
In fact, all of Christopher Robin's friends are
often found snacking on a little something. If
you're like Piglet and enjoy crunching on a haycorn,
or prefer the sharpness of a freshly picked thistle
like Eeyore, then you are a true foodie and this
book is just for you.

THE FOODIE IS USUALLY AWOKEN BY A GROWLING IN THEIR STOMACH.

Some hours later, just as the night was beginning to steal away, Pooh woke up suddenly with a sinking feeling. He had had that sinking feeling before, and he knew what it meant.

He was hungry.

WE ALL KNOW BREAKFAST IS THE MOST IMPORTANT MEAL OF THE DAY.

'When you wake up in the morning, Pooh,' said Piglet
at last, 'what's the first thing you say to yourself?'
'What's for breakfast?' said Pooh.
'What do you say Piglet?'
'I say, I wonder what's going to happen exciting to-day?'
said Piglet.
Pooh nodded thoughtfully.
'It's the same thing,' he said.

YOU CAN'T BE A NORMAL, FUNCTIONING HUMAN UNTIL AFTER MEALTIMES.

And Tigger said that ... Tiggers were
only bouncy before breakfast, and
that as soon as they had had a few haycorns
they became Quiet and Refined.

WHEN YOU HAVEN'T EATEN, YOU MAKE SURE EVERYONE KNOWS IT.

Tigger explained to anybody who was listening that he hadn't had any breakfast yet.

YOU MEASURE TIME BY THE NEAREST MEAL.

'Yes,' said Pooh. 'We had breakfast together
yesterday. By the Pine trees.
I'd made up a little basket, just a little fair-sized basket,
an ordinary biggish sort of basket, full of-'

YOU'RE MORE THAN HAPPY TO FEED A FRIEND IN NEED.

'Shall I look, too?' said Pooh, who was beginning to feel a little eleven o'clockish. And he found a small tin of condensed milk, and something seemed to tell him that Tiggers didn't like this, so he took it into a corner by itself, and went with it to see that nobody interrupted it.

YOU'LL DO ANYTHING TO GET OUT OF A PLAN THAT CONFLICTS WITH ELEVENSES.

'Well,' said Pooh, 'at eleven o'clock – at eleven o'clock – well, at eleven o'clock, you see, I generally get home about then. Because I have One or Two Things to Do.'

A FRIEND WHO SHARES YOUR CRAVINGS IS A FRIEND WORTH HAVING.

*Pooh always liked a little something
at eleven o'clock in the morning, and he
was very glad to see Rabbit getting out
plates and mugs.*

SOMETIMES ADVENTURING HAS TO WAIT UNTIL YOU'VE HAD A LITTLE SOMETHING.

'Talking about large somethings,' he went on dreamily, 'I generally have a small something about now – about this time in the morning,' and he looked wistfully at the cupboard in the corner of Owl's parlour; 'just a mouthful of condensed milk or what-not, with perhaps a lick of honey –'

YOU HATE HAVING TO CHOOSE BETWEEN YOUR FAVOURITE FOODS.

When Rabbit said, 'Honey or condensed milk with your bread?' he was so excited that he said, 'Both,' and then, so as not to seem greedy, he added, 'But don't bother about the bread, please.'

SOMETIMES YOU FIND YOURSELF IN TRICKY SITUATIONS ...

*'It all comes,' said Rabbit sternly, 'of eating
too much. I thought at the time,' said Rabbit,
'only I didn't like to say anything,' said Rabbit,
'that one of us was eating too much,' said Rabbit,
'and I knew it wasn't me,' he said.*

... BUT YOU HAVE YOUR PRIORITIES RIGHT ...

Then he thought another long time, and said:
'And the only reason for being a bee that I know of is
making honey.' And then he got up, and said:
'And the only reason for making honey is
so as I can eat it.'

... NEVER MIND THE CONSEQUENCES.

'It all comes, I suppose,' he decided, as he said good-bye to the last branch, spun round three times, and flew gracefully into a gorse-bush, 'it all comes of liking honey so much.'

YOU CAN NAME THE EXACT LOCATION OF ALL YOUR FAVOURITE TREATS ...

'That's funny,' he thought. 'I know I had a jar of honey there. A full jar, full of honey right up to the top, and it had HUNNY written on it, so that I should know it was honey. That's very funny.'

... ALTHOUGH PUTTING THEM ON THE TOP SHELF MIGHT HAVE BEEN A MISTAKE.

He could see the honey, he could smell the honey, but he couldn't quite reach the honey.

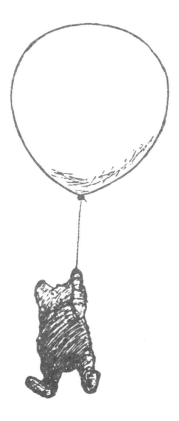

You're always trying to get fussy eaters to try new things.

And as soon as they sat down, Tigger took a large
mouthful of honey ... and he looked up at
the ceiling with his head to one side, and made
exploring noises with his tongue, and considering
noises, and what-have-we-got-here noises ...
and then he said in a very decided voice:
'Tiggers don't like honey.'

YOU APPRECIATE FRIENDS WHO PUT ON A SPREAD.

'Let's go and see everybody,' said Pooh. 'Because when you've been walking in the wind for miles, and you suddenly go into somebody's house, and he says, "Hallo, Pooh, you're just in time for a little smackerel of something," and you are, then it's what I call a Friendly Day.'

WHEN IT COMES TO FOOD, ALWAYS BE PREPARED.

'Dear, dear,' said Pooh, 'I didn't know it was as late as that.' So he sat down and took the top off his jar of honey. 'Lucky I brought this with me,' he thought. 'Many a bear going out on a warm day like this would never have thought of bringing a little something with him.' And he began to eat.

YOU GO TO EXTREME LENGTHS NOT TO SHARE YOUR FOOD.

He took his largest pot of honey and escaped with it to a broad branch of his tree, well above the water, and then he climbed down again and escaped with another pot ... and when the whole Escape was finished, there was Pooh sitting on his branch, dangling his legs, and there, beside him, were ten pots of honey.

WHEN IT'S GETTING NEAR TO TEATIME IT'S HARD TO PAY ATTENTION.

'A lick of honey,' murmured Bear to himself, 'or – or not, as the case may be.' And he gave a deep sigh, and tried very hard to listen to what Owl was saying.

THE BECKONING CALL OF AN EVENING MEAL WILL ALWAYS GUIDE YOU HOME.

'Now then, Piglet, let's go home.'
'But, Pooh,' cried Piglet, all excited,
'do you know the way?'
'No,' said Pooh. 'But there are twelve pots of
honey in my cupboard, and they've been calling to
me for hours. I couldn't hear them properly
before because Rabbit would talk, but if nobody
says anything except those twelve pots, I think,
Piglet, I shall know where they're
coming from. Come on.'

You're a connoisseur of fine food ...

As soon as he got home, he went to the larder;
and he stood on a chair, and took down a
very large jar of honey from the top shelf.
It had HUNNY written on it, but, just to
make sure ... he put his tongue in, and took
a large lick. 'Yes,' he said, 'it is. No doubt about that.
And honey, I should say, right down
to the bottom of the jar.'

... AND WOULDN'T DREAM OF GOING TO BED ON AN EMPTY STOMACH.

Then they all went home again. And I think, but I am not quite sure, that Roo had a hot bath and went straight to bed. But Pooh went back to his own house, and feeling very proud of what he had done, had a little something to revive himself.

BUT YOU ALWAYS KNOW THAT THERE'S ANOTHER MEAL JUST A SLEEP AWAY.

'Well,' said Pooh, it's the middle of the night,
which is a good time for going to sleep.
And to-morrow morning we'll have some
honey for breakfast. Do Tiggers like honey?'
'They like everything,' said Tigger cheerfully.

ABOUT A.A.MILNE

A.A.Milne was born in London in 1882. He began writing as a contributor to *Punch* magazine, and also wrote plays and poetry. Winnie-the-Pooh made his first appearance in *Punch* magazine in 1923. Soon after, in 1926, Milne published his first stories about Winnie-the-Pooh, which were an instant success. Since then, Pooh has become a world-famous bear, and Milne's stories have been translated into approximately forty different languages.

About E.H.Shepard

E.H.Shepard was born in London in 1879. He won
a scholarship to the Royal Academy Schools and
later, like Milne, worked for *Punch* magazine, as
a cartoonist and illustrator. Shepard's witty and
loving illustrations of Winnie-the-Pooh and his
friends in the Hundred Acre Wood have become
an inseparable part of the Pooh stories, and his
illustrations have become classics in their own right.

COLLECT ALL FOUR BOOKS

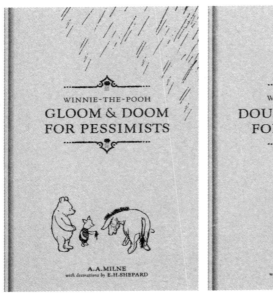

WINNIE-THE-POOH

GLOOM & DOOM
FOR PESSIMISTS

A.A.MILNE
with decorations by E.H.SHEPARD

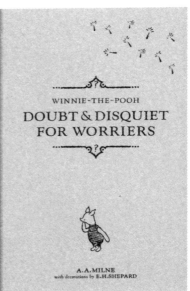

WINNIE-THE-POOH

DOUBT & DISQUIET
FOR WORRIERS

A.A.MILNE
with decorations by E.H.SHEPARD

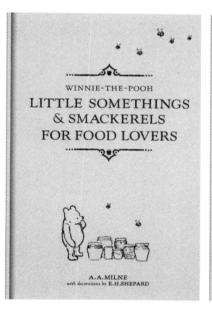

WINNIE-THE-POOH

LITTLE SOMETHINGS & SMACKERELS FOR FOOD LOVERS

A.A.MILNE
with decorations by E.H.SHEPARD

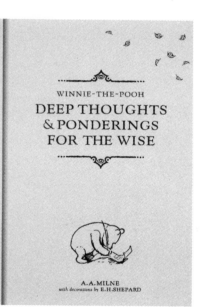

WINNIE-THE-POOH

DEEP THOUGHTS & PONDERINGS FOR THE WISE

A.A.MILNE
with decorations by E.H.SHEPARD